7. Butterfly Song

Butterfly, butterfly, butterfly, butterfly,
Oh, look, see it hovering among the flowers,
It is like a baby trying to walk and not knowing how to go.
The clouds sprinkle down the rain.

Acoman Indian
translated by Frances Densmore

8. Butterfly Dreams

I do not know
whether I was then a man dreaming I was a butterfly,
or whether I am now a butterfly
dreaming I am a man.

Chuang Tse, 4th Century B.C.

Acknowledgements

Butterfly Dreams by Chuang Tse
Text used with the kind permission of Jane English and Carol Wilson
www.eheart.com

4 Haikus:

Over the Dianthus by Kokku

Butterfly in my hand by Buson

The flying butterfly by Issa

It has no voice anon.

Taken from the book 'The Spirit of Butterflies – Myth, Magic & Art',
by Maraleen Manos-Jones.
Published in November 2000 by Harry. N. Abrams Inc.

The Butterfly by Pavel Friedmann. Taken from the book
'The Punished Land', translated by Dennis Silk, published by Viking

Butterfly Song from Acoman Indian. Taken from 'The Oxford Book of
Verse in Translation', translated by Frances Densmore

This work was commissioned by Brighton Chamber Choir, who gave the first performance on 11th May 2003, at The Old Market, Hove, Sussex, conducted by Paul Brough.

Duration: c. 14 minutes

Score on sale: Order No. CH66418

BUTTERFLY DREAMS

from an idea by Alan Barrett

COMPOSER'S NOTE

Which am I really? A butterfly dreaming that I am a man, or a man dreaming that I was a butterfly?

The answer is neither of these: there were two unreal modifications of the Single Being, of the universal norm, in which all beings in all their states are one.

Chuang Tse, 4th Century B.C.
from Guénon Multiple States of Being

Alan Barrett suggested that I write a piece for Brighton Chamber Choir based on his selected texts, and reflecting his photographs of butterflies.

I regard *Butterfly Dreams* as a sacred work. The Red Indians have the pure metaphysics of virgin nature, and insofar as virgin nature is a manifestation of the *Logos* (the Word of God), *Butterfly Dreams* is intrinsically a sacred work. The texts are taken from different sources, including Chuang Tse, an Acoman Indian and a poem written by a young Czech victim of Auschwitz. All the poems share an almost child-like simplicity, and I have tried to reflect this in the music, which should be sung as simply and naturally as possible.

Butterfly Dreams is dedicated to William Two-Feather, a medicine man from the Apache Indian tribe, who brought me the gift of a pow-wow drum that had been used in the sacred ceremonies of the Apache Indians, such as the Sun Dance. It is also dedicated to Alan Barrett, and to Brighton Chamber Choir, who gave the first performance.

J.T.

for William Two-Feather,
and for Brighton Chamber Choir and Alan Barrett

BUTTERFLY DREAMS

Songs for a Butterfly

John Tavener

1. Butterfly Dreams based on Chuang Tse

Magical and exquisite (♩ = 40)

CH66418

4
S 1
then a man dream - ing I was a but - - - - - - - ter -
S 2
then a man dream - ing I was a but - - - - - - - ter -
S 3
I was then a man dream - ing I was a but - - - - - -
S 4
I was then a man dream - ing I was a but - - - - - -
A 1
then a man dream - ing I was a but - - - - - - - ter -
A 2
I was then a man dream - ing I was a but - - - - - -
T 1
then a man dream - ing I was a but - - - - - - - ter -
T 2
I was then a man dream - ing I was a but - - - - - -
B 1
then a man dream - ing I was a but - - - - - - - ter -
B 2
I was then a man dream - ing I was a but - - - - - -

6
S 1
fly, or whe - - - ther I am
S 2
fly, or whe - - - ther I am
S 3
- - ter - fly, or whe - - - ther I
S 4
- - ter - fly, or whe - - - ther I
A 1
fly, or whe - - - ther I am
A 2
- - ter - fly, or whe - - - ther I
T 1
fly, or whe - - - ther I am
T 2
- - ter - fly, or whe - - - ther I
B 1
fly, or whe - - - ther I am
B 2
- - ter - fly, or whe - - - ther I

9
S 1
niente
now a but - ter - fly dream - - - - - - ing I am a man.
S 2
niente
now a but - ter - fly dream - - - - - - ing I am a man.
S 3
niente
am now a but - ter - fly dream - - - - - - ing I am a man.
S 4
niente
am now a but - ter - fly dream - - - - - - ing I am a man.
A 1
niente
now a but - ter - fly dream - - - - - - ing I am a man.
A 2
niente
am now a but - ter - fly dream - - - - - - ing I am a man.
T 1
niente
now a but - ter - fly dream - - - - - - ing I am a man.
T 2
niente
am now a but - ter - fly dream - - - - - - ing I am a man.
B 1
niente
now a but - ter - fly dream - - - - - - ing I am a man.
B 2
niente
am now a but - ter - fly dream - - - - - - ing I am a man.

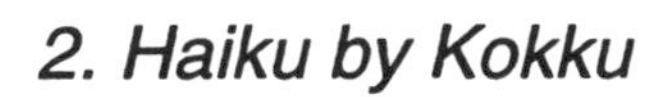
2. Haiku by Kokku

♩= 60
S 1
S 2
A 1
A 2
T 1
T 2
B 1
B 2
mp
p (shadowing)
O - ver the Di - an - thus. See. A white but - ter - fly,
5
whose soul I won - der.

3. Haiku by Buson

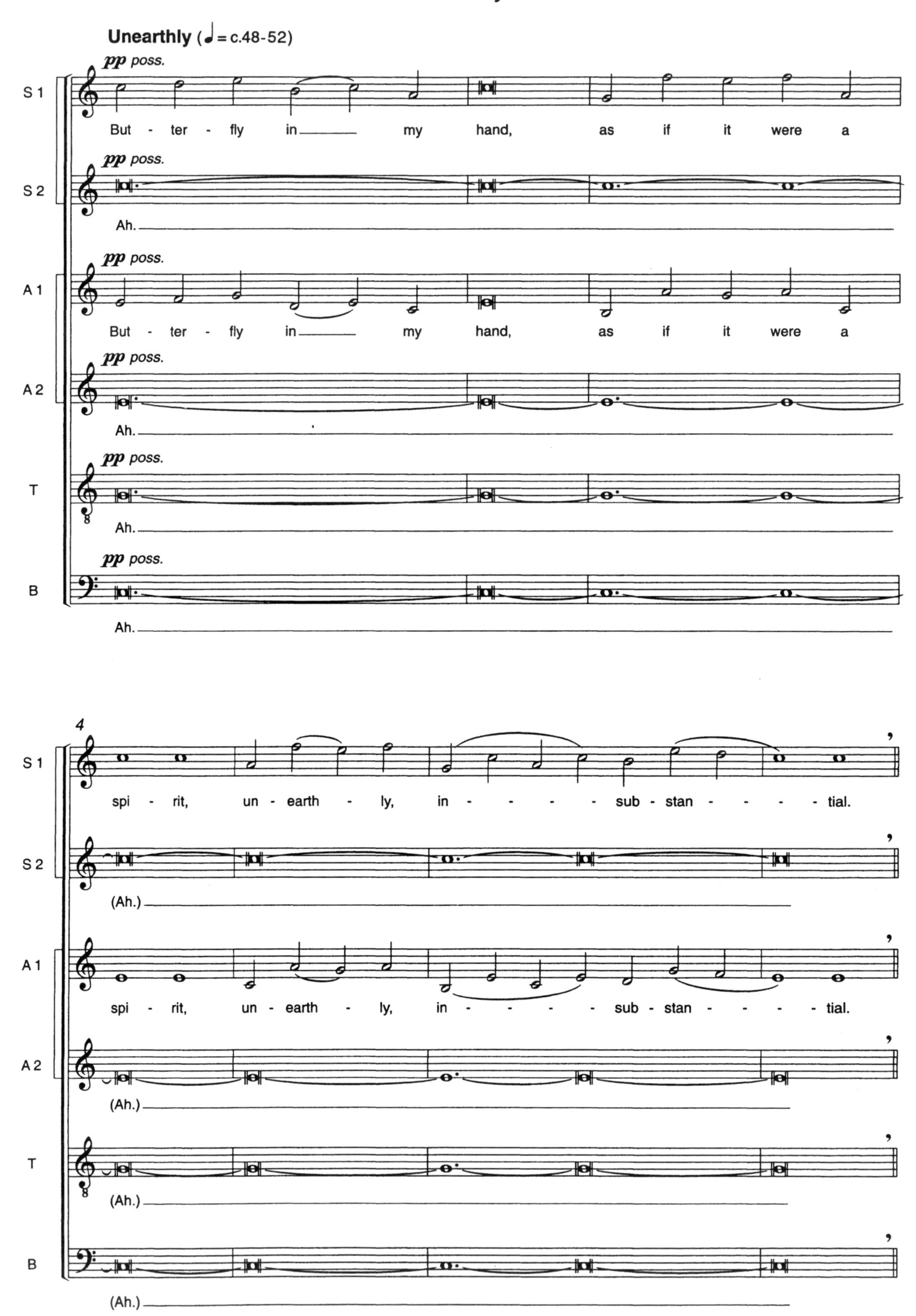

4. Haiku by Issa

3
(cresc.)
molto
ff
S 1
S 2
S 3
A 1
A 2
A 3
T 1
T 2
T 3
B 1
B 2
B 3
fp cresc.
of dust.
ture of dust.
ture of dust.
ture of dust.
ture of dust.
ture of dust.
crea ture of dust.
fp
self a crea ture of dust.

5
S 1
pp
sim.
fp cresc.
The fly-ing but-ter-fly, I feel my-self a crea - - - - - - - ture of dust.
S 2
pp
sim.
fp cresc.
The fly-ing but-ter - fly, I feel my-self a crea - - - - - - - - ture of dust.
S 3
pp
sim.
fp cresc.
The fly-ing but-ter-fly, I feel my-self a crea - - - - - - - - ture of dust.
A 1
pp
sim.
fp
The fly-ing but-ter - fly, I feel my - self a crea - - - - - - - - ture of dust.
A 2
pp
sim.
The fly-ing but-ter-fly, I feel my-self a crea - - - - - - - - ture
A 3
pp
sim.
The fly-ing but-ter - fly, I feel my - self a crea - - - - - - -
T 1
pp
sim.
The fly-ing but-ter-fly, I feel my-self a crea - - - - -
T 2
pp
sim.
The fly-ing but-ter - fly, I feel my - self a crea - - - -
T 3
pp
sim.
The fly-ing but-ter-fly, I feel my-self a crea -
B 1
pp
sim.
The fly-ing but-ter - fly, I feel my-self a crea -
B 2
pp
sim.
The fly-ing but-ter-fly, I feel my-self a
B 3
pp
sim.
The fly-ing but-ter-fly, I feel my-

7
(cresc.)
molto ff
S 1
S 2
S 3
A 1
A 2
A 3
T 1
T 2
T 3
B 1
B 2
B 3
fp cresc.
of dust.
ture of dust.
- - ture of dust.
- - - - ture of dust.
- - - - - ture of dust.
- - - - - - - - ture of dust.
crea - - - - - - - - - - ture of dust.
self a crea - - - - - - - - - - ture of dust.

9
pp
sim.
fp
cresc.
S 1
The fly-ing but-ter-fly, I feel my-self a crea - - - - - - - ture of dust.
S 2
The fly-ing but-ter - fly, I feel my - self a crea - - - - - - - - ture of dust.
S 3
The fly-ing but-ter-fly, I feel my-self a crea - - - - - - - - ture of dust.
A 1
The fly-ing but-ter - fly, I feel my - self a crea - - - - - - - ture of dust.
A 2
The fly-ing but-ter-fly, I feel my-self a crea - - - - - - - ture
A 3
The fly-ing but-ter - fly, I feel my - self a crea - - - - - - -
T 1
The fly-ing but-ter-fly, I feel my-self a crea - - - - -
T 2
The fly-ing but-ter - fly, I feel my - self a crea - - -
T 3
The fly-ing but-ter - fly, I feel my-self a crea -
B 1
The fly-ing but-ter - fly, I feel my-self a crea -
B 2
The fly-ing but-ter-fly, I feel my-self a
B 3
The fly-ing but-ter-fly, I feel my-

11
(cresc.)
molto ff
S 1
S 2
S 3
A 1
A 2
A 3
T 1
T 2
T 3
B 1
B 2
B 3
fp cresc.
of dust.
ture of dust.
- - ture of dust.
- - - - - ture of dust.
- - - - - - ture of dust.
- - - - - - - ture of dust.
crea - - - - - - - - - ture of dust.
self a crea - - - - - - - - - ture of dust.

13
S 1
pp
sim.
fp
cresc.
The fly-ing but-ter-fly, I feel my-self a crea - - - - - - - ture of dust.
S 2
pp
sim.
fp
cresc.
The fly-ing but-ter-fly, I feel my-self a crea - - - - - - - ture of dust.
S 3
pp
sim.
fp
cresc.
The fly-ing but-ter-fly, I feel my-self a crea - - - - - - - ture of dust.
A 1
pp
sim.
fp
The fly-ing but-ter-fly, I feel my - self a crea - - - - - - ture of dust.
A 2
pp
sim.
The fly-ing but-ter-fly, I feel my-self a crea - - - - - - ture
A 3
pp
sim.
The fly-ing but-ter - fly, I feel my-self a crea - - - - - -
T 1
pp
sim.
The fly-ing but-ter-fly, I feel my-self a crea - - - - -
T 2
pp
sim.
The fly-ing but-ter-fly, I feel my-self a crea - - -
T 3
pp
sim.
The fly-ing but-ter-fly, I feel my-self a crea -
B 1
pp
sim.
The fly-ing but-ter-fly, I feel my-self a crea -
B 2
pp
sim.
The fly-ing but-ter-fly, I feel my-self a
B 3
pp
sim.
The fly-ing but-ter-fly, I feel my-

15
(cresc.)
molto ff
S 1
S 2
S 3
A 1
A 2
A 3
T 1
T 2
T 3
B 1
B 2
B 3
fp cresc.
of dust.
ture of dust.
ture of dust.
ture of dust.
ture of dust.
ture of dust.
crea - ture of dust.
self a crea - ture of dust.

5. Haiku, anon.

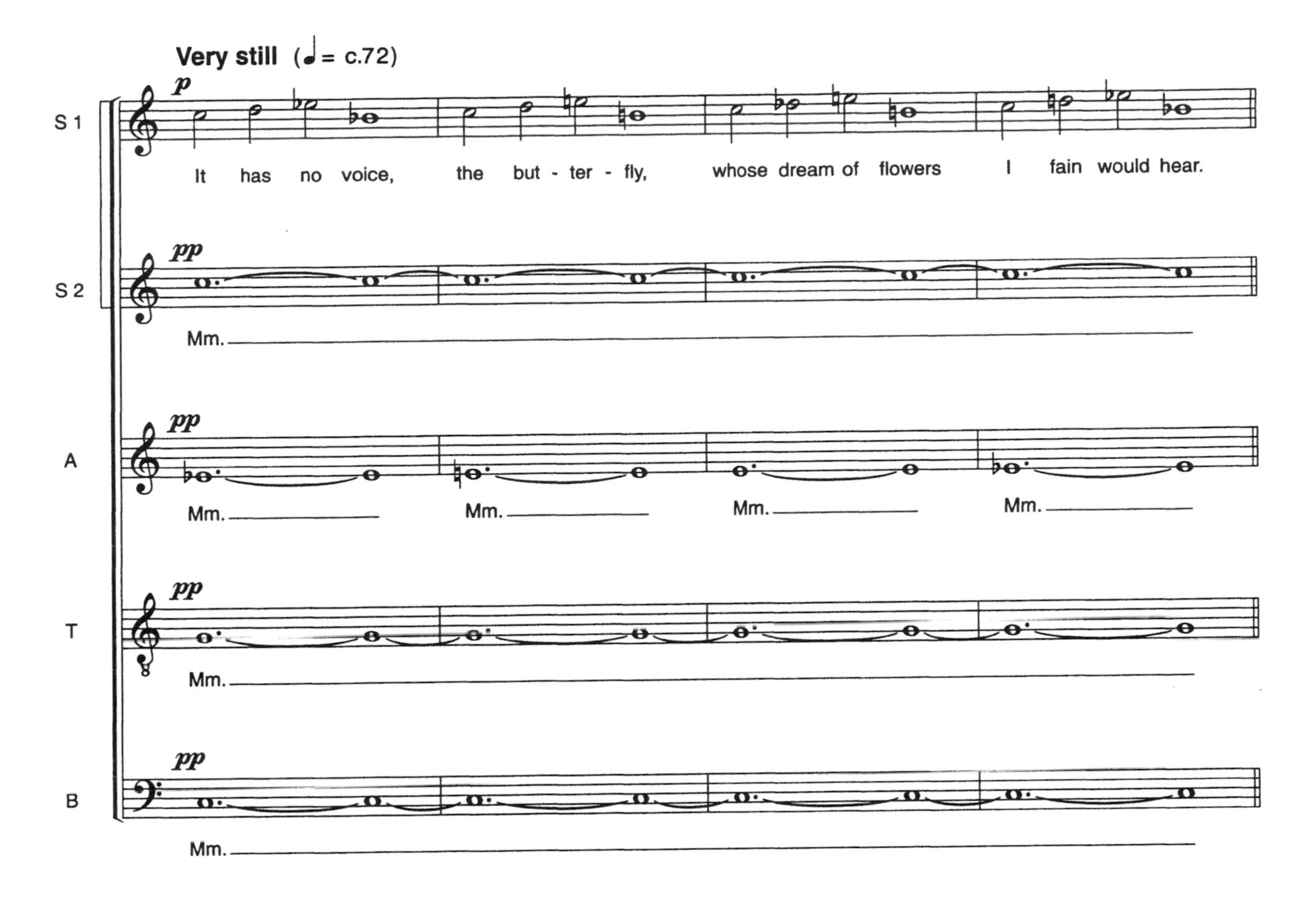
Very still (♩= c.72)
S 1
S 2
A
T
B
p
pp
It has no voice, the but - ter - fly, whose dream of flowers I fain would hear.
Mm.

6. The Butterfly by Pavel Friedmann

rit.
13
cresc. molto f pesante
S
he wan - ted To kiss the last of my world.
A
he wan - ted To kiss the last of my world.
T
he wan - ted To kiss the last of my world.
B
he wan - ted To kiss the last of my world.
A tempo
molto f, con molto intensità
17
S
I have been here se - ven weeks. Ghet - - - to - ized.
A
I have been here se - ven weeks. Ghet - - - to - ized.
f
T
Oh.
B
Oh.

20
sub. pp
without emotion
S
Who loved me found me, Dai - sies call to me,
A
Who loved me found me, Dai - sies call to me,
T
Who loved me found me, Dai - sies call to me,
B
Who loved me found me, Dai - sies call to me,

24
cresc. poco a poco, con molto intensità
S
And the bran - ches al - so of the white chest - nut in my yard.
A
T
Oh.
B
27
(cresc.)
molto f
But I ha - ven't seen a but - ter - fly here. That last one was the last one.
3

31
sub. pp
cresc.
molto
rit.
f pesante
poco
There are no but - ter - flies, here, in the ghet - to.

7. Butterfly Song from Acoman Indian

Haunting, simple, primordial (♩ = c.60)

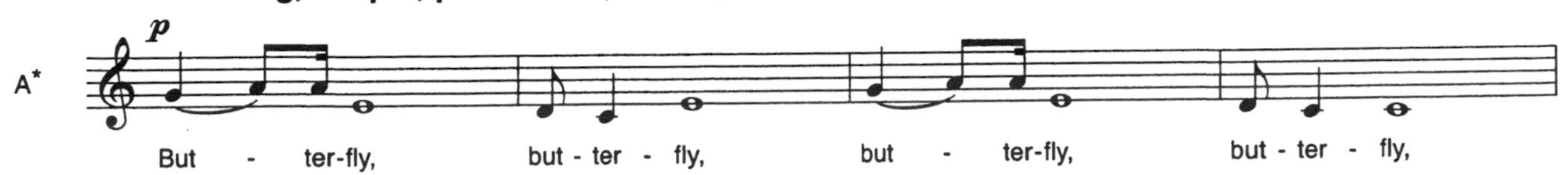
p
A*
But - ter-fly, but - ter - fly, but - ter-fly, but - ter - fly,

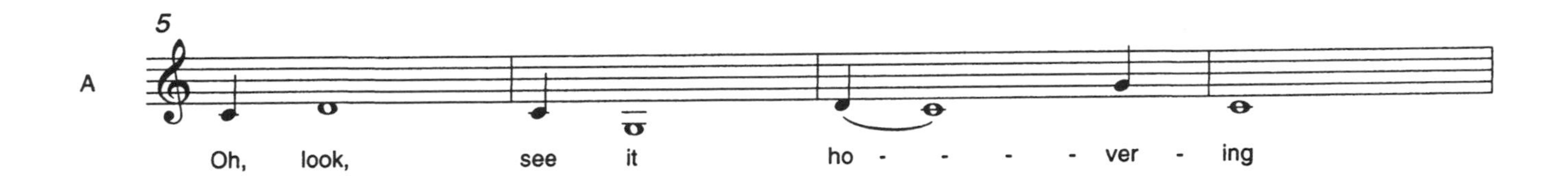
5
A
Oh, look, see it ho - - - - ver - ing

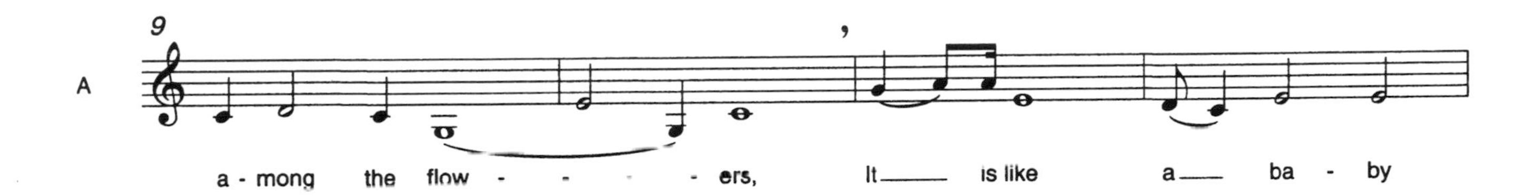
9
A
a - mong the flow - - - - ers, It is like a ba - by

13
A
try - ing to walk and not know - ing how to go.

17
A
The clouds sprin - - - - kle down the rain.

* If wished, this movement may be sung by a soloist.

8. Butterfly Dreams based on Chuang Tse

4
S 1
then a man dream - ing I was a but - - - - - - - ter -
S 2
then a man dream - ing I was a but - - - - - - - ter -
S 3
I was then a man dream - ing I was a but - - - - - -
S 4
I was then a man dream - ing I was a but - - - - - -
A 1
then a man dream - ing I was a but - - - - - - - ter -
A 2
I was then a man dream - ing I was a but - - - - - -
T 1
then a man dream - ing I was a but - - - - - - - ter -
T 2
I was then a man dream - ing I was a but - - - - - -
B 1
then a man dream - ing I was a but - - - - - - - ter -
B 2
I was then a man dream - ing I was a but - - - - - -

6
S 1
fly, or whe - - - ther I am
S 2
fly, or whe - - - ther I am
S 3
- - ter - fly, or whe - - - - ther I
S 4
- - ter - fly, or whe - - - - ther I
A 1
fly, or whe - - - ther I am
A 2
- - ter - fly, or whe - - - - ther I
T 1
fly, or whe - - - ther I am
T 2
- - ter - fly, or whe - - - - ther I
B 1
fly, or whe - - - ther I am
B 2
- - ter - fly, or whe - - - - ther I